Meet Elsa

Elsa became Queen of Arendelle when her parents were lost at sea.

She was born with the power to manipulate ice and snow and used these to entertain her sister, Anna.

When Elsa accidentally hurt Anna with her powers, she shut herself away from the world, so she couldn't cause any harm.

After her powers were exposed, Elsa fled Arendelle, but with Anna's help she learnt how to control and appreciate her powers, restoring summer to the kingdom.

Elsa is strong-willed, artistic and reserved, until Anna's love removes her fears.

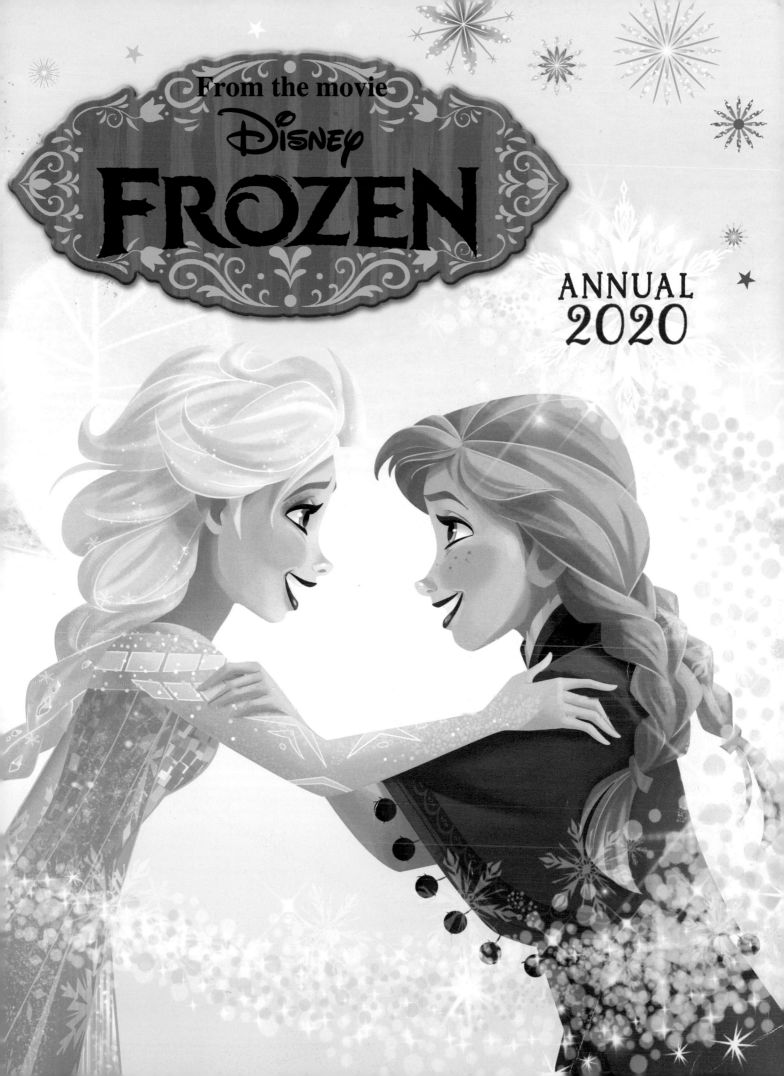

Contents

Snowy Surprise

Can you spot 6 differences in picture B? Colour in a snowflake for every difference you find. The first one has been done for you.

Snow Angel

Tick the piece that is missing from the picture!

A	B
C	D

A

B

Answers on page 68.

Meet Anna

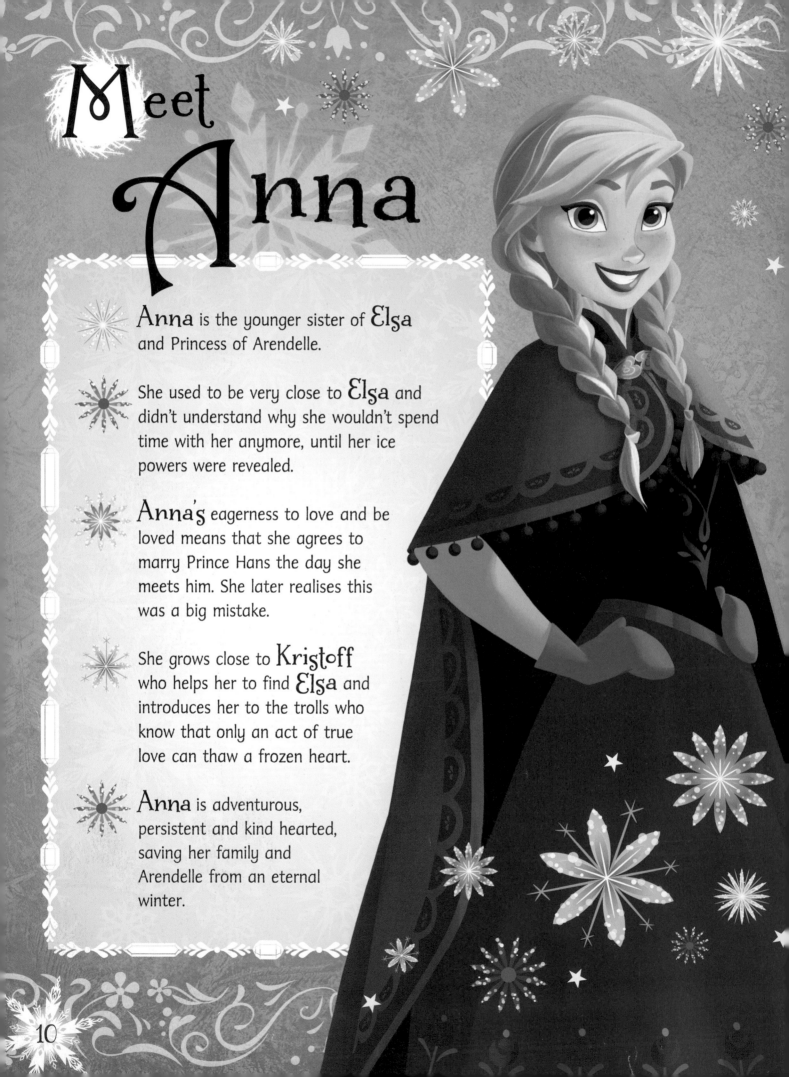

- **Anna** is the younger sister of **Elsa** and Princess of Arendelle.

- She used to be very close to **Elsa** and didn't understand why she wouldn't spend time with her anymore, until her ice powers were revealed.

- **Anna's** eagerness to love and be loved means that she agrees to marry Prince Hans the day she meets him. She later realises this was a big mistake.

- She grows close to **Kristoff** who helps her to find **Elsa** and introduces her to the trolls who know that only an act of true love can thaw a frozen heart.

- **Anna** is adventurous, persistent and kind hearted, saving her family and Arendelle from an eternal winter.

Best Friends

Anna and Elsa
are best friends!
Colour them
in brightly.

11

Meet Kristoff and Sven

- **Kristoff** is an Ice Harvester who goes everywhere with his loyal reindeer, **Sven**.

- He was brought up in the mountains by the trolls and prefers the company of his reindeer to humans.

- When **Kristoff** meets **Anna**, he agrees to take her to the North Mountain in return for supplies, but he begins to care for her.

- Despite his tough exterior, he wants to ensure that **Anna** is safe and to help her find and save her sister, **Elsa**.

- **Kristoff** is strong, kind and loyal and, along with his adventurous reindeer, **Sven**, becomes the best of friends with **Anna**.

Dressing Up

Help Sven dress up as Olaf! Draw the missing items in the grid, so that each appears once in each row and column.

Meet Olaf

★ Olaf was created by Elsa's ice powers when she was a child.

★ He lives in the cold and snowy mountains, but he dreams of summer.

★ Olaf meets Anna, Kristoff and Sven in the mountains and agrees to lead them to Elsa's ice palace.

★ He is very loyal and optimistic, helping Anna to realise what she must do to save Elsa and herself.

★ Olaf is a happy little snowman who loves warm hugs, but needs to be careful he doesn't melt, until Elsa makes him his own snow cloud.

Draw and Play with Olaf

Have fun with your friends! Everyone chooses an outline of Olaf.
Take turns rolling the dice, and draw on the missing parts that match the number rolled
(see the guide below). The first person to complete Olaf, wins.

Pillow Fight

It's time for bed but Anna and Elsa still want to play! Match the pairs of feathers from the pillow fight!

Snowman Friend

Elsa made the sisters a snowman! Spot its matching shadow below.

A

B

C

D

E

F

G

H

Answers on page 68.

17

Dancing Days

Manuscript: Alessandro Ferrari; Layout: Elisabetta Melaranci; Cleanup: Federica Salfo; Colour: Dario Calabria, Stefania Santi

WHAT A BEAUTIFUL MORNING! I LOVE BEAUTIFUL MORNINGS! DON'T YOU, OLAF?

YES I DO, ANNA.

AND I BELIEVE THESE ICE SCULPTURES DO, TOO!

WAIT, WHAT'S HAPPENING HERE? ELSA MADE A LOT OF THEM...

DON'T YOU LIKE THEM? I LOVE THEM, THEY'RE SO BEAUTIFUL!

I THINK SOMETHING IS GOING ON WITH MY SISTER...

"LET'S GO FIND HER..."

ELSA? ARE YOU HERE?

18

ANNA! WHAT A SURPRISE!

WHAT'S GOING ON?

WHY? WHAT DO YOU MEAN? NOTHING IS GOING ON.

COME ON! THESE SCULPTURES ARE EVERYWHERE IN THE CASTLE!

WELL... NEXT WEEK THE **PRINCES** OF FIVE KINGDOMS WILL COME TO **ARENDELLE** AND I'LL HAVE TO DANCE WITH THEM... BUT I CAN'T DANCE VERY WELL, SO...

... I MADE THESE STATUES SO I COULD SEE THE MOVES AND LEARN THEM!

DON'T YOU WORRY, ELSA... I'LL TEACH YOU HOW TO DANCE!

19

IT'S NOT EASY...

"... BUT IF YOU KEEP PRACTISING..."

SOMEONE STOOOOP ME!

"... AND PRACTISING..."

"... YOU'LL FINALLY MASTER IT!"

YES! I CAN DANCE!

I CAN DANCE, TOO! I'M A DANCING SNOWMAN!

GREAT! NOW YOU'RE READY...

To be continued...

Party Plans

Anna and Elsa are ready for a celebration at the palace.

Flower Code

A   C   E   H

K   L   O   T

Use the picture code to write the name of Anna's pudding in the spaces below.

_____ _____ _____ _____ _____ _____ _____ _____ _____

_____ _____ _____ _____

Ice Shadow

Look at the ice sculpture Elsa has created and find its shadow below.

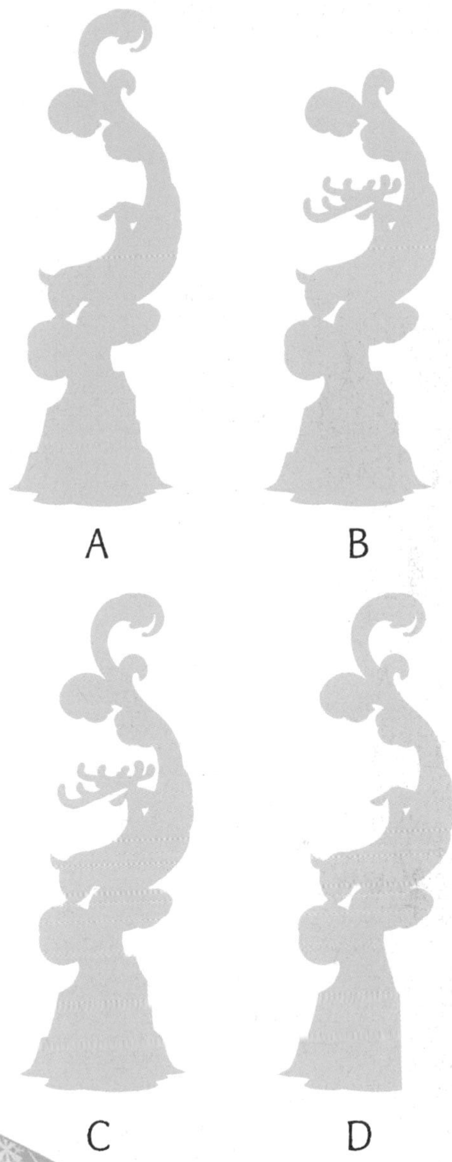

A

B

C

D

Dancing Days

PART TWO

"... FOR YOUR OFFICIAL DANCING DAY!"

YOUR MAJESTY...

YOUR HIGHNESS...

BUT AS SOON AS THEY START...

OW!

I'M TERRIBLY SORRY, YOUR MAJESTY. I MUST CONFESS... I AM NOT AS GREAT A DANCER AS YOU ARE!

ACTUALLY, QUEEN ELSA...

... NEITHER AM I!

I NEVER LEARNT, EITHER!

WE ARE SO ASHAMED...

!

!

WELL... WHAT ABOUT SKATING, INSTEAD? ?

THE END

Elsa's Surprise

Elsa's magic keeps Olaf cool! Can you add some more cool colours to the picture?

The New Gloves

Manuscript: Tea Orsi; Layout: Nicoletta Baldari; Colour: Dario Calabria

ANNA HAS JUST KNITTED A NEW PAIR OF MITTENS...

TA-DAH! DO YOU LIKE THEM?

THEY'RE LOVELY!

AND THEY LOOK EXACTLY LIKE SVEN!

YEAH, I KNOW...

AND I ALSO MADE THESE!

WOW! THEY LOOK LIKE OLAF!

THAT'S WHY I LOVE BOTH PAIRS... AND I DON'T KNOW WHICH ONES TO WEAR!

WELL, MAYBE I KNOW WHAT WE CAN DO...

ELSA TELLS ANNA ABOUT HER IDEA AND...

YOUR MITTENS ARE AMAZING!

YOU'RE THE BEST SISTER EVER, ELSA!

WINK

THE END

27

Sail Away

Anna, Elsa and Olaf are sailing back to Arendelle but some of their things have fallen overboard! Tick off the items as you pass them along the right path home.

Flying Friends

These friendly birds are following the boat. Can you spot them in the scene?

START

FINISH

A Special Teacher

Manuscript: Tea Orsi; Layout: Emilio Urbano; Clean-up: Manuela Razzi; Colours: Patrizia Zangrilli and Luca Merli

HELLO!

HI!

PRINCESS ANNA?!?

CALL ME ANNA! WHAT'S YOUR NAME?

I'M MATHILDE, YOUR MAJES-- ERM... ANNA!

WHY AREN'T YOU ICE SKATING, MATHILDE?

BECAUSE I CAN'T!

AND... ALSO... I'M AFRAID OF FALLING DOWN...

BUT SLIDING ON THE ICE IS FUN! I DO IT WITH NO SKATES!

OH, YES! THERE'S NOTHING TO BE AFRAID OF, IF YOU ARE CAREFUL!

SWIIISH

LATER...

HERE IS YOUR ICE SKATING TEACHER, MATHILDE.

WELCOME, MATHILDE! ARE YOU READY TO START?

QUEEN ELSA!

THERE'S NOTHING TO BE AFRAID OF HERE.

YOU'RE GOING TO LOVE IT!

HOORAY!

FINALLY, MATHILDE PUTS HER SKATES ON AND...

UGH! ICE IS SO SLIPPERY!

HA, HA! I KNOW!

EVERYONE JOINS IN...

SWISH
SWOOSH

LOOK AT US! THIS IS WHAT YOU SHOULDN'T DO!

BEND YOUR KNEES SLIGHTLY AND MOVE ONE FOOT AT A TIME!

OOOOKAY!

THUD

I ALWAYS FALL, BUT I KEEP PRACTISING!

SOON, MATHILDE GAINS MORE CONFIDENCE...

I LOVE SKATING!

ME TOO!

AND YOU'RE BOTH IMPROVING A LOT!

GO MATHILDE, GO!

YOU'RE SO GOOD!

SWISH

HOW DID YOU LEARN TO SKATE SO WELL?

QUEEN ELSA TAUGHT ME! AND HER FRIENDS HELPED.

I WANT TO LEARN FROM THEM, TOO!

CAN YOU GIVE US A LESSON?

HUH?!?

IT'LL BE A PLEASURE TO HAVE SO MANY LOVELY STUDENTS!

YAY! MORE LESSONS!

HOORAY!

I THINK I **LOVE** BEING AN ICE SKATING TEACHER!

I DON'T KNOW WHY, BUT I WAS SURE YOU WOULD!

THE END

Tasty Treats

Trace over the letters to find out the name of the breakfast treat Elsa and Olaf are making.

Pancakes

Big Breakfast

Circle the biggest pancake.

1

2

3

4

5

Kitchen Chaos

Write the numbers from 1 to 4 to put the jumbled picture back together again.

1   2   3   4

1

Answers on page 68.

Snow Biscuits

Follow Anna's recipe to make super yummy cookies that are perfect for a festive treat!

You will need:

300g flour
1 tsp baking powder
1 tbsp milk
1 egg + 1 yolk
150g butter, cubed
225g caster sugar
100g icing sugar

Ask a grown-up to help.

1

In a large bowl mix the flour, baking powder, egg, egg yolk and butter until crumbly. Add the caster sugar gradually.

2

Knead into a dough, then wrap it with flour-sprinkled baking paper. Leave for 20 minutes.

3

Preheat the oven to 180°C or Gas Mark 4. Roll out the dough to a thickness of about 5mm.

4

Use star-shaped cookie cutters to create the biscuits. Place on a baking tray, and brush with milk.

5

Bake for 12 minutes, or until golden brown. Sprinkle with icing sugar for a snowy effect!

Spot with Olaf

Spot the 5 differences between the pictures of Olaf's favourite summer dream.

A

B

a

b

c

All Olaf's daydreams are about summer, except one. Can you find the odd one out?

d

e

f

Answers on page 69.

Race to the Castle

Anna wants to get to the ice castle, but she's not the only one! Choose your favourite character and see who's first to the finish!

START

1

2

3

4

5

14

15

16

17

18

FINISH

How to play

A game for 2 to 4 players.

You will need a counter for each player and a dice.

Choose a character and place your counter on the Start. The player with the highest number on the dice goes first. Take turns to roll the dice and move the number of spaces shown. Follow the instructions when you land on the special ice squares. The player who reaches the ice castle first, wins!

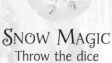

ICE SPIKES
The ice startles you! Go back 1.

SNOW MAGIC
Throw the dice again.

TROLLS
Go forward 1.

MARSHMALLOW
Oh no! Go back to the start.

CREVICE
Miss a turn.

JUMP
Go forward 2 spaces.

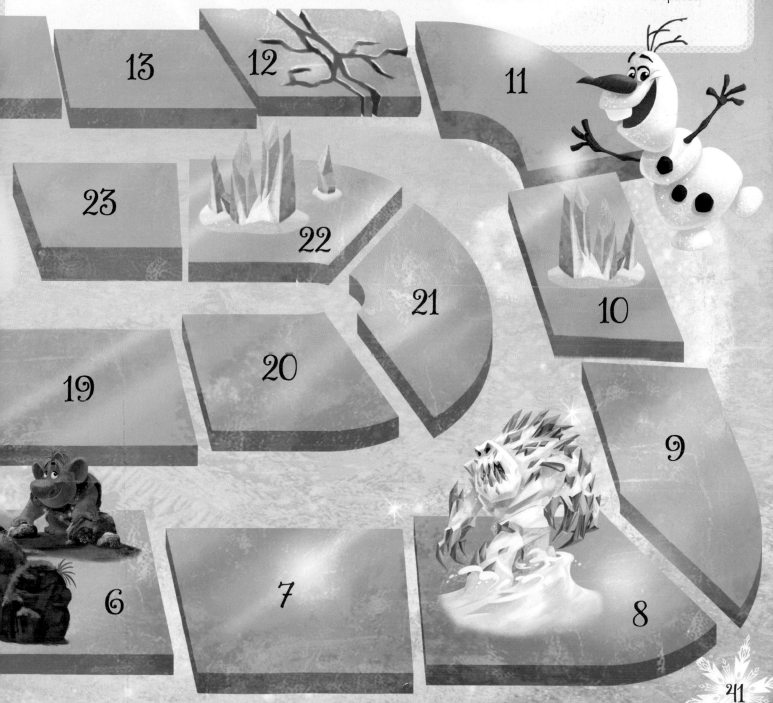

13   12   11

23   22   10

21

19   20   9

6   7   8

Frosty Fun

Kristoff and Sven have lots of ice to move. The blocks of ice are numbered from 1 to 9. Can you write the missing numbers?

1 | — | 3
— | 5 | 6
— | 8 | —

Ice Sums

Count the number of blocks of ice that are not on the pile.

Answers on page 69.

Question of Balance

Manuscript: Tea Orsi; Layout: Marino Gentile; Cleanup: Nicoletta Baldari; Paint: Dario Calabria

OLAF WANTS TO PLAY WITH A NEW SEE-SAW AND ANNA JOINS HIM.

OOPS, WE'RE STUCK!

IF ONLY SNOW WAS HEAVIER...

BOING

I KNOW WHAT TO DO!

OLAF COMES BACK WITH A LOT OF NEW "BUTTONS" BUT...

OH NO!

I'M SORRY BUT YOU'RE STILL LIGHTER THAN ME.

DON'T WORRY, I'VE GOT AN IDEA!

SOON...

WELL... NOW WE'RE STUCK THE OPPOSITE WAY!

WOW THAT WAS FUN!

True Friends

With a little magic from Elsa,
Olaf can always be with
his friends, even when
winter is over!
Have fun colouring the scene.

Dream Time

Follow these 4 simple steps to create beautiful icy decorations!

You will need:

pipe cleaners
wool
safety scissors
liquid glue
paintbrush

Ask a grown-up to help.

1

Bend the pipe cleaners into heart and star shapes. Wrap wool around the outline of each shape.

2

With the same strand of wool, weave a web inside each shape.

3

Use a paintbrush to apply a coat of glue on the shapes you have created.

4

Leave your decorations to dry, then hang them above your bed!

A Mysterious Invitation

Manuscript: Tea Orsi; Layout: Nicoletta Baldari; Cleanup: Veronica Di Lorenzo; Colour: Patrizia Zangrilli and Antonia Angrisani

ANNA IS READY TO TAKE A WALK, WHEN...

HUH?! WHAT'S A BASKET DOING THERE?

A MESSAGE?

In the woods...

IN THE WOODS?!

ANNA! LOOK! I'VE FOUND SOMETHING NEAR THE WINDOW!

HEY! YOU'VE GOT ONE, TOO!

In the woods...

THERE WAS PART OF A MESSAGE INSIDE IT!

...You'll find...

IT LOOKS LIKE THEY GO TOGETHER...

WHO WROTE THEM?

In the woods...

...You'll find...

LOOK WHAT I FOUND! WHAT DOES IT SAY?

SURELY IT WAS THE SAME PERSON, BUT... HUH?!?

IT WAS NEAR THE FLOWERS! I ALWAYS SAY HI TO THEM IN THE MORNING.

I CAN'T BELIEVE IT! YOU FOUND ONE, TOO!

AW, I CAN'T READ IT EITHER!

MAYBE IT'S WRITTEN IN CODE...

ALMOST... THIS MESSAGE IS STAINED!

...The

MAYBE THE STAIN MEANS THAT WE HAVE TO LOOK FOR... A STAIN!

I'M NOT SO SURE ABOUT THAT... BUT THE STAIN COVERS THE MOST IMPORTANT WORD IN YOUR MESSAGE!

NOW WE KNOW THAT WE'LL FIND SOMETHING IN THE WOODS...

BUT... WHAT IS THAT SOMETHING? I WANT TO KNOW!

THERE'S ONLY ONE WAY TO FIND OUT!

ANNA, OLAF AND ELSA GET READY FOR A TRIP IN THE WOODS AND...

I'D LIKE KRISTOFF AND SVEN TO BE HERE TOO, BUT I COULDN'T FIND THEM ANYWHERE!

WE'LL TELL THEM ABOUT THIS LITTLE MYSTERY TONIGHT!

I LOVE THE WOODS!

Favourite Friends

52

Dress-up Mask Crafts

To make your dress-up masks, cut them out along the dashed lines. Then thread pretty ribbon through the holes.

© 2019 Disney

PLEASE NOTE:
The mask should not be worn where vision is vital for safety, e.g. when crossing the road.

© 2019 Disney

Colour in the masks.
You could even
decorate them with
stickers.

Frozen Quiz

Read the 8 facts on the scroll, and tick whether you think they're true or false.

1 Elsa is younger than Anna   T   F

2 Elsa's birthday falls on the winter solstice   T   F

3 Anna is cheerful, brave and always on the go   T   F

4 Anna has magic powers   T   F

5 Olaf uses a snow cloud to stop him melting   T   F

6 Kristoff is Arendelle's Official Ice Harvester   T   F

7 Sven is a mountain goat   T   F

8 Marshmallow lives with Anna and Elsa in Arendelle castle   T   F

Check your answers on page 69 then write how many you got right.

Colour in the same number of hearts on the chart to find out how much of a fan you are!

LEVEL: NEED SOME WORK	LEVEL: NOT BAD!	LEVEL: SUPER!
♡ ♡ ♡	♡ ♡ ♡	♡ ♡

Answers on page 69.

DISNEY
FROZEN II

Young princesses Anna and Elsa loved listening to their parents' stories about the past. Their minds bubbled with questions about the tale of their father, King Agnarr, and the people trapped in the mist. But their parents didn't have answers.

Their mother, Queen Iduna, soothed them to sleep with a lullaby about a special river, called Ahtohallan, said to hold all the answers about the past.

"Do you think Ahtohallan knows why I have powers?" asked Elsa.

"I imagine it knows that and much more," answered the queen.

"Someone should really try and find it," Elsa said, as she closed her eyes. Iduna's smile was bitter-sweet, as she slipped out of the room.

That night, Anna awoke and called excitedly to Elsa. "The sky's awake, so I'm awake, so we have to play."

Many years had passed since then, and though their parents were gone, Anna and Elsa were incredibly close. But one night, Elsa heard a voice trying to draw her away from the kingdom. Did it belong to someone magical like her?

Elsa used her magic powers and images she had never seen before blossomed from her finger- tips. Then an enormous shockwave shot across the fjord! The rain froze into small crystals that hung suspended in the air.

The deafening sound woke Anna and she raced to the balcony, searching for Elsa. Before their eyes, Arendelle transformed. Water stopped flowing; fire vanished; the wind whirled, pushing villagers out of their homes, and the ground rippled like the sea! Through the chaos, Anna and Kristoff led everyone up to the cliffs, where Elsa told Anna about the voice. She explained that the voice hadn't said anything; it had simply showed her the Enchanted Forest.

Just then the trolls arrived. "Much about the past is not what it seems," Pabbie said. "When one can see no future, all one can do is the next right thing." Elsa knew she had to go to the Enchanted Forest and follow the voice. Pabbie told Anna to look after her sister. "I won't let anything happen to her," she promised.

Elsa was determined to set things right. Anna, Kristoff, Olaf, and Sven joined her on the journey North. As dawn broke, they spotted a wall of sparkling mist, and knew they had arrived. When Elsa approached it, she was overcome with a strange feeling and grabbed Anna's hand. As they reached the thick mist, it began to part.

The mist rolled back revealing four stone pillars, but it trapped them inside, propelling them deeper into the forest! They reached a clearing and walked through it like a dream. But then the Wind Spirit appeared, picking Olaf up! The strength of the current broke him apart, whirling him around and around. As everyone tried to help, they got swept up in the windstorm, too! Elsa used her magic to force everyone out, but she remained trapped inside the cyclone.

Elsa opened her arms, freeing herself from the Wind Spirit and a sculpture of young Prince Agnarr cradled in the arms of a Northuldra girl appeared before her. Then soldiers appeared. They were characters from their father's story! The Arendellian lieutenant, Matthias, was there and he was overjoyed to hear their father had made it back to Arendelle with the help of a Northuldra. But the two opposing sides began to argue, still at odds after so many years.

Suddenly, a bright flash appeared. The ball of fire dashed around a tree, sending it up in flames. Chaos erupted as it blazed a trail through the forest, burning everything in its path. Elsa raced behind it, using her magic to try and stop it from spreading. The Fire Spirit was a small salamander. Elsa understood its pain and fear. She gently held out her hand and it scampered onto it, enjoying her cool touch. As she helped the Fire Spirit find calm, the flames died. Then they both heard a voice calling them North.

When Anna reached Elsa, she wrapped their mother's scarf around her, comfortingly. Ryder, a young Northuldra, recognised the symbols on the scarf and the opposing sides realised the sacrifice one enemy made for another, melting their differences away. They all turned to Elsa, whose presence gave them hope that they would be able to escape.

59

Mattias shared some wisdom with Anna. "Just when you think you've found your way, life'll throw you onto a new path."

Anna remembered what Pabbie had said and knew she had to do the next right thing, but she felt concerned for Elsa.

Meanwhile, Honeymaren showed Elsa the spirits of nature symbolised on her mother's scarf. Elsa was surprised to discover there was a fifth, called the bridge. It was said to connect the magic of nature to humans, and it disappeared when people stopped listening.

Elsa knew she must continue her journey and she led Anna and Olaf north. Soon they were looking down at an old Arendellian shipwreck. Anna and Elsa gasped at the sight, realising it was their parents' ship! They found a map that proved their parents had been trying to find Ahtohallan. They were seeking answers about Elsa's magic when the waves overcame them!

"This is my fault," said Elsa, close to tears.

"If anyone can save Arendelle, restore this forest and free us, it's you," Anna said. Elsa vowed to make it across the Dark Sea and find Ahtohallan, but she had to do it alone. She created a boat which sent Anna and Olaf zipping down a path of ice.

Finally, Elsa reached the edge of the Dark Sea. Lightning flashed, revealing the Water Nokk, an enormous horse. The two battled beneath the sea! Then Elsa used her magic to make an ice bridle, grabbed the reins, and swung onto its back. At first, it bucked, but soon she was riding it to the shore. Once safely on the sand, Elsa climbed off the Water Nokk.

Meanwhile, Anna and Olaf had sailed their ice boat into the Lost Caverns. They were alone in the cave until a flurry of snowflakes appeared and an ice sculpture formed. Anna realised the sculpture explained what had happened in the forest. She remembered the advice Pabbie and Mattias had given her to do the next right thing and felt more determined than ever to help Elsa set things right.

When Elsa reached Ahtohallan, the mysterious voice quietened and for the first time in her life, she felt completely at ease. The journey had changed her. Now she had no doubt, that she and her sister could finally restore peace and harmony to the unbalanced world.

THE END

Who Are You?

Take this quiz to find out which Frozen character you're most like.

1

When friends ask you if you'd like to play a game, you:
A. Say yes, since you're always ready for some fun!
B. Only agree to play if you're sure that it's safe.
C. Say you're not really the game-playing type, but then end up having a great time.
D. Let someone else answer for you.

2

When you're at a party, you:
A. Dance!
B. Have no plans of dancing, no matter what.
C. Leave. You don't go to parties.
D. Look to see where the food is.

3

When you meet someone new, you:
A. Immediately hope you have lots of things in common. It would be great to make a new friend!
B. Try not to reveal too much about yourself.
C. Barely say hello – you have other things to do.
D. Keep to yourself, especially at first.

4

When you go shopping, you:
A. Like to be able to choose from a big selection.
B. Love when gloves are on sale – although you really don't shop much.
C. Want the prices to be fair.
D. Wait outside the store, and hope someone brings you a snack.

5

If your town is suddenly covered with ice, you:

A. Have to find a way to fix it.
B. Try to get away so you won't hurt anyone.
C. Think about how this will affect your business.
D. Try not to slip!

6

When you're faced with a huge problem, you:

A. Do your best to come up with a solution.
B. Ignore the problem, and just try to live with it instead.
C. Team up with a loyal friend who will stay with you for as long as it takes.
D. Help your friends fix it, as long as you're not in the middle of a meal.

7

What would you do if you saw a cup with some water in it?

A. Say, "That glass is half full! I love water."
B. Say, "That half-empty glass of water really needs some ice."
C. You might not notice the glass at all!
D. You wouldn't say anything, but you might tip the cup over and drink the water up off the floor!

* Mostly A *
You're positive, outgoing and care about everyone, you and Anna could be twins!

* Mostly B *
Like Elsa, you are quiet and thoughtful and always look out for your friends.

* Mostly C *
Just like Kristoff, you work hard and stand up for your friends.

* Mostly D *
You're loyal and stick with your friends through thick and thin, just like Sven.

Special Sisters

Elsa and Anna are no ordinary sisters. Colour them in with your brightest colours.

Believe
IN THE JOURNEY

True to
to
Myself

Goodbye!

DESTINY Awaits!

Answers

PAGE 9 Snowy Surprise

Snow Angel
piece A

PAGE 13 Dressing Up

PAGE 16-17 Pillow Fight

PAGE 17 Snowman Friend

Shadow c

PAGE 22-23 Party Plans

Flower Code
CHOCOLATE CAKE
Ice Shadow
Shadow c

PAGE 28 Sail Away

PAGE 36 Tasty Treats

The breakfast treat is Pancakes
Big Breakfast
Pancake 4
Kitchen Chaos

PAGE 39 Spot with Olaf

PIcture e is the odd one out

PAGE 42 Frosty Fun

1 ②　3
④　5　6
⑦　8　⑨

Ice Sums

6 blocks are not on the pile

PAGE 55 Frozen Quiz

1. FALSE   5. TRUE
2. TRUE   6. TRUE
3. TRUE   7. FALSE
4. FALSE   8. FALSE

Goodbye!